# HOW TO DESIGN AND MAKE
## YOUR OWN P C B s

D0530824

# Other Titles of Interest

# HOW TO DESIGN AND MAKE YOUR OWN P C B s

by
R. A. Penfold

BERNARD BABANI (publishing) LTD
THE GRAMPIANS
SHEPHERDS BUSH ROAD
LONDON W6 7NF
ENGLAND

© 1983 BERNARD BABANI (publishing) LTD

First Published – July 1983
Reprinted – May 1988
Reprinted – January 1990
Reprinted – January 1992
Reprinted – August 1995
Reprinted – December 1997

**British Library Cataloguing in Publication Data**
Penfold, R. A.
  How to design and make your own P.C.B.s –
  (BP121)
  1. Printed circuits. – Amateurs' manuals
  I. Title
  621.381'74    TK9965

ISBN 0 85934 096 1

Printed and bound in Great Britain by Cox & Wyman Ltd, Reading

# Preface

Like most really useful ideas the basic concept of a printed circuit board is very simple. A thin board about 1 or 2mm in thickness and made from a material having good insulating properties has small holes to take the leadout wires of components so that the components can be mounted on one side of the board, their leadout wires then trimmed on the other side of the board, and soldered to pads of copper. Tracks of copper electrically join together the copper pads (and thus also the components) in the appropriate fashion so that the correct circuit is produced. This gives very neat looking results, but is also very practical in that it is relatively difficult to make mistakes with this method of construction, and it is a physically strong method of construction with the component bodies and soldered joints on opposite sides of the board.

Some years ago when printed circuits in designs for the amateur user were relatively new it was possible to produce home-constructed boards for these designs using just a few simple tools and materials. In fact some designs were so simple that they could be made by simply cutting away unwanted areas of copper using a modelling knife and then drilling the component mounting holes! These days printed circuit designs tend to be far more complex with ever more components being accommodated by boards of ever smaller dimensions, and while some boards can be produced using simple methods, an increasing number really require more sophisticated techniques.

The purpose of this book is simply to familiarise the reader with both the simple and more sophisticated methods of producing printed circuit boards, including simple photographic methods of copying designs and producing boards. In fact probably all the methods of copying and producing boards will be dealt with.

It is not difficult to design printed circuit boards for simple electronic projects, and after gaining a little experience at printed circuit design more complex boards can be tackled with confidence. Advice on designing your own boards is given in the final chapter of this book.

The subject is not covered in a vague and purely theoretical manner which leaves the reader familiar with printed circuit techniques but no wiser as far as actually building a board is concerned. The emphasis of this book is very much on the practical aspects of printed circuit design and construction with detailed instructions being given where appropriate.

*R. A. Penfold*

# CONTENTS

## WARNING NOTE

The reader should always study and carefully follow any instructions that the manufacturers of chemicals and/or aerosols may supply with their products, especially relating to use, safety, inflammability and disposal etc.

Always make sure chemicals are clearly marked as such and are kept out of the reach of children.

# Chapter 1

## SIMPLE PCB PRODUCTION

Step one in printed circuit production is to obtain the necessary tools and materials, and we will start with those items which are essential. The most obvious of these is the printed circuit board itself, and there are actually a number of different types. The base (insulating) material is normally either fibreglass or SRBP (sheet resin bonded paper), and the latter is generally the cheaper. Nevertheless, fibreglass is probably the more popular both with industrial and amateur users since it does have one or two advantages. One is simply that it is stronger and there-fore less prone to warping and cracking than SRBP. The increased strength is also advantageous for boards that carry heavy components such as transformers. Another advantage is that fibreglass is translucent and it is usually possible to see the copper tracks from the top (component) side of the board which can be very helpful when checking and fault-finding.

However, the quality of SRBP boards is more than adequate for most purposes, and I have used this type of board extensively over a number of years without encountering any real difficulties. Advertisements often refer to board as 1mm, 1.6mm, etc., and this is simply refering to the thickness of the base material. Obviously the thicker (about 1.6 to 2mm) boards are stronger than the thinner (about 1mm) types, but the heavier quality boards are only really necessary for large PCBs, or where heavy components will be mounted on the board. For most purposes the thickness of the board is of no consequence.

Sometimes copper laminate board will be specified as one ounce quality, or perhaps two ounce quality, and this refers to the weight of the copper on one square foot of board. Most circuits handle only fairly low currents, and ordinary one ounce board is all that is required. In fact one ounce board is normally sufficient even for circuits that handle quite large currents, and it is only necessary to use a heavier grade of board if the article or book containing the PCB design specifies such a grade. Of course, a heavier grade board can be used

1

where only a light grade would suffice, but a light grade should not be used where a heavy grade is specified.

Advertisements usually state that the board is "single sided" or "double sided", and this simply means that the board is coated with copper on one side or both. Double sided printed circuit designs are not often encountered, although the number of published designs of this type does seem to be on the increase. Some double sided boards simply have a plain sheet of copper on the component side of the board, apart from small circles of copper that are removed from around component mounting holes to prevent the leadout wires from short circuiting through this sheet of copper. This sheet of copper is usually connected to the earth rail and acts as a screen to prevent instability. With other types of board it is necessary to have numerous copper tracks crossing over one another without them short circuiting together. The only way of achieving this is to take one track over another on the component side of the board so that the board insulates the tracks from one another. With some printed circuit designs, especially those for computer equipment, it is not uncommon to have a large number of copper tracks which weave their way up and down through the board. The connections from one side of the board to the other are made by drilling holes in the board which are fitted with metal pins which are soldered to the track on both sides of the board. Commercially manufactured boards sometimes achieve these through the board connections using a system known as "through plating" which avoids the need to add numerous pins to the board, but is not a practical proposition for the amateur constructor. Incidentally, double sided boards are only really necessary where a large number of track cross-overs are needed, and where only a few cross-overs are required it is much easier to simply use a few link wires on the component side of the board.

Few amateur printed circuit constructors build complex double sided boards since it is very difficult to produce good quality boards of this type, and it is certainly not a good starting point for beginners. To start with you will only need single sided board. It is possible to use double sided laminate board to produce a single sided board, but you must ensure that the copper on the component side of the board is completely removed during the etching process (which will be described later) so that there is no possibility of it producing short circuits. However, this will greatly reduce the life of the etching solution, and double sided board is normally more expensive than the single sided type, so that there is no point in buying the double sided type initially unless it happens to be available at a bargain price.

Some component suppliers sell off-cuts of copper laminate board at quite reasonable prices and it is well worthwhile having a stock of boards of various sizes. Unless you are likely to build a number of large boards it is not advisable to buy large pieces of copper laminate since these are awkward to cut down into small pieces without producing a large amount of wastage.

### Resist and Etchant

The basic way in which a printed circuit board is made is to cover the areas of copper which are required on the finished board with an etch resist, and to then immerse the board in etchant which removes the unwanted (exposed) areas of copper. The etch resist is then removed to reveal the copper tracks and pads.

Anything that will keep the etchant away from the areas of copper that are to be left after etching can be used as the resist, and the most commonly used resists are water resistant paints and inks. Water soluable types are totally unsuitable since they will simply dissolve in the etching solution. A paint or ink that dries rapidly is preferable since it avoids having to wait for hours before the board can be etched. Even the more simple printed circuit designs seem to have a substantial number of thin copper tracks in a fairly small area of board these days, and a paint brush capable of producing very fine lines is required. An alternative is to simply use an exhausted fibre-tip pen (a fine point type) in paint brush fashion, and this can produce excellent results in practice even though it may not seem to be a very elegant solution to the problem.

A better way of applying the resist is to use one of the etch resist pens that are readily available from a number of component retailers. These usually have a fine point which enables thin tracks to be drawn with ease. There are actually pens for other purposes which seem to function extremely well as etch resist pens, and the fine point pens used with overhead projection equipment are a good example of the type of pen that can be used. Any pen which has a spirit based ink and a fine point should be usable in this application, but if you are in doubt about the suitability of a pen you can always draw out a few lines on a scrap of copper laminate board and then etch the board to see if the ink keeps the etchant at bay properly.

Another form of resist are the rub-down etch resistant transfers that are sold by many component retailers and which can give really excellent and professional results. These will be considered in more detail later on.

There are a number of chemicals which can be used as the etchant, but most of these are dangerous for one reason or another and are not really suitable for home-constructed boards. The etchant normally used for home produced boards is ferric chloride, and although this is less dangerous than most of the alternatives, it is still a chemical that should be used with caution.

It is not a chemical that attacks skin in the same way as an acid, but if any does get onto skin and is not washed off it will produce a yellow coloured stain and will also produce at least slight soreness. It should therefore always be washed off immediately with plenty of warm water if you get any onto your skin. It is not likely to damage clothing if any should be accidentally spilt onto your clothes, but it will be much more easily removed if it is washed off before it dries out. Even so the yellow stain may be difficult to remove, and it is advisable to wear old clothes when using this chemical.

Ferric chloride is highly corrosive to many metals, and it can react quite violently if it comes into contact with certain metals (aluminium for example). It should not be stored in metal containers, and should not be used where it could accidentally splash onto metal objects and damage them.

As ferric chloride is poisonous (and in use it gradually becomes replaced by copper chloride which is also highly poisonous) it should obviously be kept well away from food and utensils etc. used with food.

4

Ferric chloride can be purchased in a number of different forms, and the most convenient type to get is a ready made solution of the chemical. Several component retailers sell it in this form; usually in 250ml bottles and in a concentrated form. It should be diluted slightly before use, and will probably be supplied with directions stating the degree of dilution. It will not need very much dilution, and a 250ml bottle usually gives only 500ml or a litre when diluted as directed.

A few suppliers sell ferric chloride in the form of crystals, or "Ferric Chloride Rock" as it is sometimes called. This name is quite appropriate as in this form it does look like chunks of yellow rock rather than small neat crystals, and it is literally rock hard. In this form ferric chloride is usually sold in 500gm packs, and this is sufficient to make one litre of etching solution. It can also be obtained in much larger packs, but as 500gm is sufficient to etch quite a large number of average size boards and is likely to last even an industrious constructor quite a long time it is probably not worthwhile obtaining substantially more than 500gm at a time.

In its crystaline form ferric chloride does not dissolve particularly easily, but if stirred at least periodically it should eventually dissolve fully, and with continuous stirring it should dissolve reasonably rapidly. Using warm water helps to make the chemical dissolve a little more readily and rapidly.

Finally, ferric chloride can be obtained in anhydrous form, which simply means its pure ferric chloride without any water content. It does have a certain amount of water in its crystaline form incidentally. The anhydrous form is not as widely available as it once was, and is not very popular since it is relatively difficult to use in this form. Anhydrous ferric chloride looks like a fine black powder, and one of the problems with this form of the chemical is that when handling it there is a risk of some of the powder being released into the air. Breathing in this powder is very unpleasant to say the least, and in this form it is necessary to handle the chemical very carefully indeed.

What really makes this form of ferric chloride so difficult to use is the heat that is produced when it comes into contact with water. Even starting with chilled water it can rapidly become heated to the point where the container in which it is mixed becomes too hot to touch, and there is a danger of melting plastic containers. Another problem is that of getting the chemical to dissolve properly and produce a good etching solution. For some reason it seems to be possible to end up with a substantial amount of chemical which will not dissolve, plus a solution that looks like ferric chloride but has little or no etching capacity.

I could NOT RECOMMEND the use of anhydrous ferric chloride, but if you do decide to use this form of the chemical the following method is probably the best one to adopt. Carefully place some of the chemical in a dish, and preferably a large dish so that a fairly thin layer of the chemical (say about 5mm or so) will give a reasonable amount of ferric chloride. If this is then left to stand for several hours, preferably with the chemical being stirred slightly every half hour or so, the anhydrous ferric chloride will absorb moisture from the air and will gradually go a yellow-brown colour. Eventually it will go noticeably wet with a strong solution forming in the bottom of the container. At this stage it should be possible to add cold water to the dish and dissolve the rest of the chemical to produce a reasonably strong solution suitable for use as an etchant. It is still likely that a certain amount of heat will be generated when the water is added, which is why cold water (preferably chilled with ice cubes) should be used. It is also likely that there will be a small amount of chemical that will not dissolve, and this can either be filtered from the solution, or as it does not seem to hinder etching it can just be left in the solution.

### Drills

Probably most prospective printed circuit constructors will have some means of drilling holes in copper laminate board, but unfortunately few will be equipped with drills capable of making the minute component mounting holes. The standard diameter for component mounting holes is 1mm, although a few components such as some preset resistors, large electrolytic capacitors, etc. require a slightly larger diameter. A mounting hole diameter of about 1.4mm is suitable for such components. Some constructors prefer to use a diameter of less than 1mm for semiconductors and certain other components which have very thin leadout wires, and 0.7mm or 0.8mm is a suitable diameter for these components. It is quite possible and acceptable to use 1mm diameter mounting holes for these components, and the only slight disadvantage in doing so is that the leadout wires will be slightly loose in the mounting holes which results in a slightly weaker mechanical construction, and it may also be marginally more difficult to produce good soldered joints between the leadout wires and copper pads.

Ordinary hand and electric drills are really intended for use with drill bits of about 2mm and larger, and it may be difficult to use these with drill bits as small as 0.7mm to 1.4mm. In fact many full size drills simply will not close down far enough to take drill bits as small as this. There are ways around this problem, and winding thin (about 40 swg) wire around the shank of the drill to effectively increase its diameter will usually enable it to be fitted tightly into a full size drill. There are also drill bits of suitable sizes which have wide shanks of around 2 to 2.5mm in diameter, and there should be no difficulty in fitting these into most full size hand or electric drills.

Provided you obtain good quality drill bits they should be quite tough, but obviously drill bits of only around 0.7mm to 1.4mm in diameter can only have a limited amount of strength and should be treated reasonably carefully. Provided they are only treated to downwards pressure there should be no problems, but if the drill bit is not at right angles to the board a neat hole will not be produced and it is quite likely that the drill bit will be snapped in two. You must therefore take reasonable care when drilling holes with such small drill bits, and if possible electric drills should be used in a stand.

Ideally a miniature electric drill should be used when drilling the component mounting holes, and I would strongly recommend the use of a stand with one of these. Several of the larger component retailers sell one or more drills of this type plus suitable matching stands, and these really are the ideal tool for this application. The initial cost of a drill, stand, and a suitable power supply (most run off a 12 volt DC supply and not direct from the mains) may be quite high, but for anyone who is going to produce a substantial number of printed circuit boards over a period of time it should certainly be well worth the expenditure. Incidentally, it may not be necessary to obtain a power supply for the drill if you already have a bench power supply since this may well be able to supply the correct voltage at a suitable current. Most drills require about 12 to 14 volts DC at a maximum current of about 1.5 to 3 amps (depending on the power of the drill).

A slight drawback of fibre glass copper laminate board is its tendency to rapidly blunt ordinary twist drills. Fibre glass board consists of a plastic material which is not in itself very tough or strong, but which is reinforced by thousands of tiny glass filaments which give the board immense strength. It is this glass content, and its extreme hardness, which results in the drill bits becoming blunted after perhaps no more than a few dozen holes have been drilled.

A few component retailers sell special miniature drill bits which are made from an extremely hard material and which therefore last much longer when used to drill fibre glass boards. The drills of this type I have used do indeed seem to have much longer working lives than ordinary HSS twist drills, although the special types are usually about four or five times more expensive than standard twist drills which partially offsets any saving in cost.

Some of these special drill bits are somewhat more brittle than normal HSS twist drill bits, and bearing in mind that they are also relatively expensive they should obviously be treated with more care than usual. In fact many drill bits of this type are really only intended for use in an electric drill mounted in a stand.

## Making a Board

We have now covered the main items that are needed when making a printed circuit board, and there are one or two other odds and ends that are required. These are simple household items though, and these will be introduced as we progress through the etching process.

There are actually several different ways of producing a

8

printed circuit board, although they are all essentially the same and the main differences are simply the order in which the various steps in the process are carried out. We will therefore start by considering one method of producing a board, and then a few alternative methods will be described.

The first task is to consult the book or magazine in which the printed circuit is given in order to determine the size of the board. You will normally have a circuit diagram, a component layout diagram, and the printed circuit pattern reproduced actual size, as in Figures 1, 2 and 3 respectively. This circuit is for a signal tracer, and is taken from book No. BP98 "Popular Electronic Circuits – Book 2" which is by the same publisher and author as this book. This circuit was chosen more or less at random and the printed circuit design was produced for this publication just to act as a simple example of a practical PCB. The size of the printed circuit may be specified in the text or on one of the drawings, but in most cases it will be necessary to take measurements from the actual size copper track pattern diagram. Note that the insides of the corner markers represent the outside edges of the board, and in this case the board measures 2.7 inches by 1.5 inches. It will not normally matter if the board is cut slightly too large, although in some projects the board fits into guide rails inside the case (rather than being bolted in place) and in such cases it is obviously necessary to cut the board accurately to size if it is to fit into place properly.

SRBP and fibre glass boards can both be cut to size using a hacksaw. Mark out the extremities of the final board on the copper side of the laminate board, and then draw a second set of lines about 2mm or so outside these. By carefully cutting between these lines it should be possible to produce a piece of board with good accuracy and straight sides without too much difficulty. The edges of the board can be smoothed and given a better finish using a small flat file, and with fibre glass board this gets rid of the rough edges which are undesirable since you can easily get a cut from these if you are not careful. Note that the copper laminate is marked on the copper side and sawn from this side to reduce the risk of lifting the copper coating away from the base material when cutting the board. For this reason the board should always be cut and drilled from the

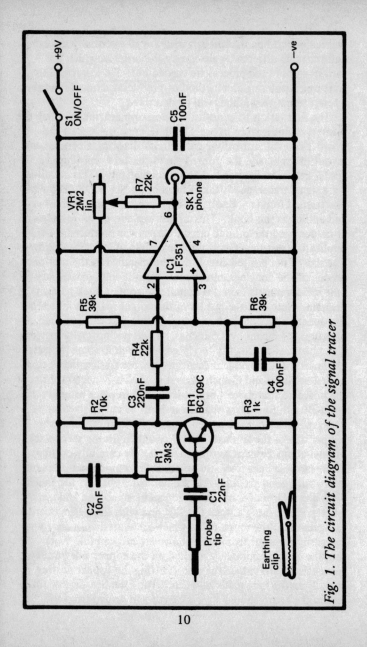

Fig. 1. The circuit diagram of the signal tracer

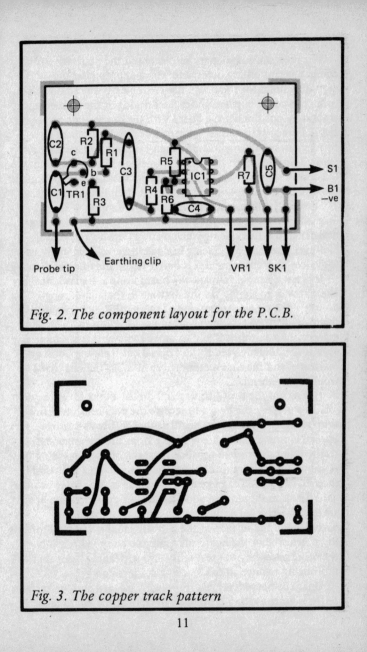

*Fig. 2. The component layout for the P.C.B.*

*Fig. 3. The copper track pattern*

copper side.

The next stage is to mark on the board the positions of the component mounting holes, and where appropriate, the mounting holes for the board itself. The easy way to do this is to fix the board in place under the drawing of the copper track, accurately positioning the board with the copper side uppermost. Using a bradawl or similar pointed tool the positions of the component mounting holes are then carefully and accurately marked through onto the board by making small indentations in the copper. As well as acting as markers these also help to guide the drill bit accurately into position when drilling the holes.

Obviously this method results in slight damage to the magazine or book, and you may therefore prefer to trace the design and use this tracing when marking the hole positions. However carefully the tracing is made there will inevitably be some loss of accuracy and it is better to use the original drawing.

It is not essential to mark the board using a bradawl, and an alternative is to simply fix the drawing to the board using double sided tape or something of this nature, and then drill through the drawing which is itself used to provide the drilling markers. Again this is likely to prove somewhat less accurate even if the drawing used is the original cut from the book or magazine, and the first method given above is the one that I would recommend.

Having cut the board to size and drilled all the holes the next job is to prepare the board to receive the etch resist, and this simply entails cleaning the board as thoroughly as possible. Special cleaning blocks are available from a few component retailers and these seem to work very well. It will probably be possible to find suitable cleaning materials in most households though, and something like a scouring pad or a cleaning powder used for sinks should give good results. Copper laminate boards are usually received with a certain amount of oxide and corrosion on the surface of the copper, and it is essential for this to be removed or the board may fail to etch properly. It is therefore necessary to use a fairly strong cleaning agent that will thoroughly remove all oxide, dirt and corrosion.

Once the board has been thoroughly cleaned and the surface of the copper coating is shiny all over, rinse the board under hot water to remove any final traces of the cleanser or grease that might be on the board, and then be careful not to touch the copper surface of the board. If you do touch the copper you will leave greasy finger marks which could hinder the etching process, and patches of moisture could be left on the board, causing it to quickly produce a thin layer of oxide which again could hinder etching.

The next step is simply to use the etch resist to draw copper pads around the component mounting holes, and then to draw in the copper tracks to join up the pads in the correct manner. You must obviously try to keep your hands off the copper surface of the board while doing this, and with larger boards it can be helpful to place a piece of paper or cloth on part of the board so that you can reset a hand on the board without actually touching it, but make sure that the cloth or paper is grease and moisture free. Start along the top edge of the board and work methodically down through the board, rather than simply working randomly (which would probably lead to errors and smudging of parts of the board that had already been completed).

Some modern printed circuit designs are so intricate that they can be very difficult indeed to copy. When producing a board of this type it is essential to use a printed circuit resist pen (or a suitable substitute) having a very fine point, and where there are several thin, closely spaced tracks running side-by-side use a ruler to enable good straight lines to be drawn. Otherwise it may not be possible to fit them all in without overlaps occuring. If tracks or pads should merge together, wait for the resist to dry and then use a compass point or other fine pointed implement to scrape away the unwanted resist.

Using a resist pen and similar methods of applying the resist it is not really possible to produce quite the quality of a board made using more sophisticated techniques. However, with care it is possible to obtain good neat results, and even if the board is not particularly neat it will work just as well as any other board provided you are careful to avoid breaks in tracks, merged tracks and pads, and errors in the track pattern. Always thoroughly check the resist pattern against the copper track drawing to ensure that no errors have been produced. If any are spotted at this stage they can easily be corrected by allowing the resist to dry, scraping off the incorrect sections of resist, and then adding in the correct ones. If numerous mistakes are made it is probably better to remove all the resist and start again. If errors are not spotted until the finished board fails to work it means a lot of wasted work in producing a board that will probably be unusable. If there is only a minor mistake it is possible to cut pieces of track that are incorrect using a sharp modelling knife, ensuring that a small piece of track is removed so that there is definitely no connection through the track, and then link wires can be used to connect the pads together correctly. Pieces of insulating sleeving can be used to prevent accidental short circuits if necessary. Obviously this does not give a particularly neat finished project, although it should work reliably, but if a number of mistakes are made there will probably be no alternative to removing all the components from the board and constructing a new one. A few minutes checking the board before etching it is clearly time well spent.

Once the resist has dried and the board has been checked and corrected if necessary, the next step is to immerse the board in the etchant until all the exposed copper has been removed. Basically what happens during etching is that the copper replaces the iron in the ferric chloride to produce copper chloride, and the iron is precipitated. Initially etching takes place quite rapidly and may take just a few minutes, but as the ferric chloride gradually becomes replaced with copper chloride the etching process gradually becomes slower, and after a number of boards have been etched it will be found that the etching time is very prolonged, or is not completed at all, and the etchant has to be replaced. Ferric chloride is a red-yellow colour, and copper chloride is blue, so that with use the etching solution gradually goes more and more green in colour, and this gives warning that the chemical is nearing the end of its working life before the etching time becomes greatly lengthened or etching practically ceases altogether.

When etching the board you can simply place it copper side uppermost in a non-metalic dish of adequate size, add a good covering of etching solution, and inspect the board periodically until etching has been completed. A major drawback of this system is that a layer or iron and copper chloride tends to form on the surface of the board and this greatly extends the etching time. Gently rocking the dish helps to dispel this layer and considerably reduce the etching time, although this task can quickly become rather tedious.

There are alternative methods which give a fast etching time with little or no agitation of the board and etchant. There are excellent commercially produced etching kits available (the "SENO GS" system for example) which are based on a heavy gauge polythene bag plus rods and plastic clips which can be used to seal and divide the bag. The basic idea is that the ferric chloride crystals in the bag are dissolved in the appropriate amount of water, the board is then placed into the etchant, and the bag is sealed to prevent accidental spillage. It is usually quite easy to arrange things so that the board is in a roughly vertical position with the copper side of the board facing downwards if the board is not perfectly vertical. In this position etching takes place quite quickly since the iron precipitate tends to fall downwards away from the board, and etching is not inhibited by a thick layer of iron and copper chloride. However, occasional agitation of the board and etchant will still help to disperse any slight inhibiting layer that might build up, and should give a small further reduction in the etching time.

Once the board has been fully etched it is moved up to the top part of the polythene bag, and then the bag is sealed across the middle so that the etchant is trapped in the bottom section of the bag and the board is in a separate compartment at the top. The top of the bag is then opened, the top section of the bag (and thus the board as well) are rinsed with water to remove any traces of etchant, and then the board is removed. Provided due care is taken, this system permits rapid etching with a minimum of trouble and mess.

There are other ways of obtaining more rapid etching with only occasional agitation, and any system that has the board in a vertical position or with the copper side facing down into the etchant should give good results. Figure 4 illustrates a couple of simple ways of achieving this. In Figure 4(a) a rounded dish is used so that the board is held in place at the four corners, and is not in contact with the dish at any other points. This is

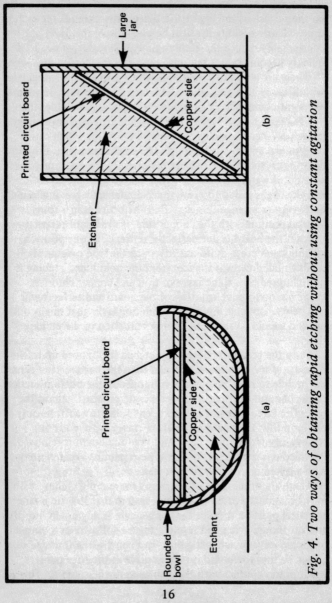

*Fig. 4. Two ways of obtaining rapid etching without using constant agitation*

important, and it is unlikely that satisfactory results will be obtained if the board is simply placed copper side down in a flat bottomed dish. The copper surface of the board would probably be in contact with the bottom of the dish in places, and there would be very little etchant between the board and the dish over the rest of the board's area. This would prevent or seriously slow down the etching process, and would probably be worse than simply leaving the board copper side uppermost in the dish.

When using this method of etching it is advisable to first immerse the board in the etchant copper side up to ensure that the board is properly covered with etchant and that no air bubbles are present on the surface of the board. These would prevent etching from occuring on the affected parts of the board, and must be avoided if possible. Having ensured that the copper side of the board has been properly covered with etchant, if the board is then turned over and the etchant is briefly agitated there is little risk of any air bubbles being left on the copper side of the board.

The method shown in Figure 4(b) is most useful for larger boards which would require an impractically large dish to permit the method shown in Figure 4(a). The jar needs to be quite large, and something like an old instant coffee jar is suitable. Quite a lot of etchant will be needed in order to nearly fill the jar, and it might be necessary to use in excess of one litre. This may be a little expensive initially, but the etchant will of course last proportionately longer than a smaller amount. A smaller amount of etchant could be diluted sufficiently to fill the jar, but this might substantially slow down etching and is not recommended.

With very large boards the only practical way of etching the board may be to use a large flat dish (such as a photographic dish) with the board placed copper side uppermost, and frequent agitation being used to prevent the etching time from being excessively long. Etching takes place most rapidly on parts of the board where there are only small areas of exposed copper, and takes much longer on parts of the board where there are comparatively large expanses of exposed copper. Etching also occurs more rapidly around the edges of the board

17

than it does near the centre of the board. Because of these factors it can take quite a time (perhaps an hour or more) to fully etch a very large board.

You can try methods of holding the board copper side down in the dish, and about 5 to 10mm clear of the bottom of the dish, so that etching is speeded up. One way of achieving this is to use pieces of Bostik Blue Tak or plasticine to act as spacers on the underside of the board, but this is only really practical for board where there are areas of board at suitable places and of adequate size that are covered with resist. The plasticine or Bostik Blue Tak should not be placed on areas of the board where the copper is exposed since the etchant would obviously be prevented from reaching the (would-be) areas of exposed copper.

A system which works better and is generally more convenient in practice is shown in Figure 5. Here two wooden or plastic rods are placed along the length of the dish, on opposite sides, and are somewhat longer than the dish so they they rest on top. The board is then suspended from the rods on two lengths of wire, one at each end of the board. Only one wire is shown in Figure 5 for the sake of clarity, incidentally. The best wire to use is a fairly heavy gauge of single strand wire (say about 18 or 20 swg) which is PVC covered. Enamelled copper wire is suitable provided there is no damage to the enamel insulation, but non-insulated wire should not be used (for the simple reason that the etchant would almost certainly attack and eat through the wire!). The wires are fixed to the rods merely by winding the ends of the wires around the rods a couple of times. Allow the wires to loop down beneath the board and do not attempt to flatten the wires against the underside of the board, otherwise there is a danger of hindering or preventing etching where the wires are in contact with the board.

If it is necessary to etch a board copper side uppermost in a dish it will probably be found that swabbing the copper side of the board with a piece of cottonwool occasionally helps to considerably speed up the etching process. The etching time is to some extent dependent on the temperature of the etching solution, and using a warm solution should also help to reduce this.

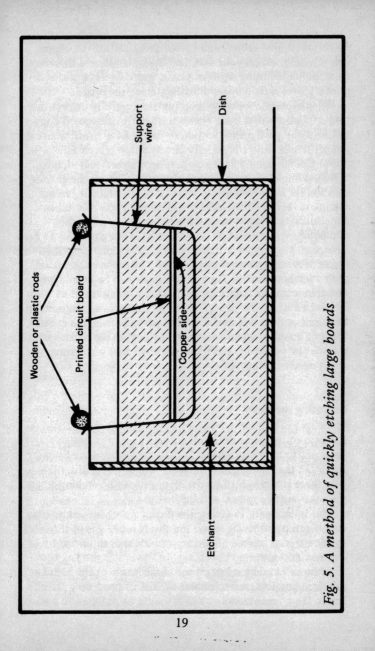

Fig. 5. A method of quickly etching large boards

19

As mentioned earlier, you should avoid getting the copper chloride solution on your skin, and the board should therefore be manipulated using a pair of plastic (not metal) tweezers, or plastic gloves should be worn when etching the board.

When etching appears to be complete, carefully inspect the board to ensure that there are no small areas of exposed copper left, and pay particular attention to parts of the board where the copper tracks and pads are very closely spaced (such as clusters of IC pads). Once you have ascertained that etching is fully completed, hold the board vertically above the etching solution for a few seconds to let most of the etchant run off the board, and then wipe the board using a piece of kitchen paper or something of this nature to remove most of the remaining etching solution. Incidentally, it is a good idea to keep a piece of kitchen paper handy during the etching process so that traces of etching solution can be wiped from the tweezers or gloves when necessary. The board should then be thoroughly rinsed in water to wash away any last remaining traces of etching solution. Be careful not to get the etching solution onto steel sinks as you will find that once partially used the etchant tends to leave a copper coating on any ferrous metal with which it comes into contact, and it also seems to have a corrosive effect on ferrous metal.

## Removing the Resist

The final task before the board is ready for the components to be soldered in place is to remove the resist which might otherwise severely hinder the process of making good quality soldered joints to the copper tracks. You can buy resist remover, and this is a light spirit which will dissolve most paints and inks. It is also possible to buy printed circuit polishing blocks which are also suitable for removing the resist. Another method is to use a scouring pad or powder, and this is really one of the more simple parts of printed circuit production that should not really give any difficulties.

In order to make soldering the components to the board as simple as possible, and to reduce the risk of producing "dry" joints, the copper tracks and pads should be polished to a good finish before fitting the components in place. However, it is almost certain that removing the resist will leave a good dirt and corrosion-free surface, and once again, there should be no difficulties here.

The copper side of the board can be coated with a flux lacquer which prevents the copper tracks and pads from becoming dirty or oxidized once they have been cleaned. A flux lacquer also aids good soldered joints when the components are connected to the board. However, it is by no means essential to use such a treatment on the finished board, and using modern components and solders there should be no difficulty in soldering the components into place if this is done as soon as the board has been finished, or if it is cleaned and polished before fitting the components in place. It is advantageous to use a flux lacquer in that it prevents severe corrosion of the copper tracks over a period of time, and the possibility of the tracks failing to provide a good conductive path.

## Summary

To summarise then, the basic stages in producing a printed circuit board are as follows:—

1. Cut the board to size using a hacksaw.
2. Clean the copper side of the board thoroughly to give a clean highly polished surface.
3. Mark the positions of the mounting holes using a bradawl or similar pointed implement.
4. Drill the holes in the board.
5. Apply the etch resist, check the track pattern, correct any mistakes or places where pads or tracks have merged together.
6. Once resist has dried, etch the board in ferric chloride solution.
7. Wash and thoroughly clean the board to remove both the etchant and resist.
8. If desired, coat the board with a flux lacquer.
9. Solder the components into place.

**Variations**

As was pointed out earlier, there are methods of producing printed circuit boards that are basically the same as the method just described, but differ in a few points of detail, and we will now consider these.

It is not essential to drill the holes in the board before applying the etch resist, and drilling the holes can be the last task in the sequence prior to fitting the components. However, this method of board production is not recommended unless rub-on etch-resist transfers are used. These are sold by many electronic component retailers, and they enable neater results to be obtained than are possible using a resist pen, resist and paint-brush, or similar methods. Various types of resist transfers are available including pads of various sizes, straight tracks and curved tracks of various thicknesses, and clusters of integrated circuit pads. The latter are especially useful since they enable very accurate results to be easily obtained.

The basic procedure is much the same using rub-on resist transfers, with the first step being to cut out a board of the correct size, after which it is cleaned, and the positions of the mounting holes are marked using a bradawl or a similar tool. When marking out the positions of IC clusters it is only necessary to mark the positions of two holes (preferably diagonally opposite each other) since with two holes in the correct positions all the others will automatically be in the right positions as well.

Next the pads are rubbed down onto the board, including IC clusters. As for any other form of etch resist, try to avoid touching the board while applying the resist transfers even if this does prove to be a little awkward on occasions. It is possible to use an old fibre-tip pen or something of this nature to rub-down the transfers onto the board, but a special spatula is available and is very convenient in use. A little practice is needed in order to obtain optimum results since pressing too lightly will result in part of the transfer being left on the backing sheet when it is pulled clear of the board, while too much pressure may give a similar result with the pads becoming distorted or in some other way damaged. If a transfer is damaged

22

in some way it will usually be possible to remove it by pressing a piece of adhesive tape onto the transfer, which should then come away with the tape when it is removed. Alternatively it can be carefully scraped away using the rub-down spatula. If one or two pads of an IC cluster are damaged, in the interest of obtaining optimum accuracy it is advisable to remove all the pads in the cluster and then apply a new cluster to the board.

Next the tracks are rubbed-down into position, and there should be no problem here if the board is quite simple and only has straight tracks. With curved tracks things can be a little more difficult with the curves of the rub-on track transfers not necessarily fitting nicely into the layout you are trying to copy. However, transfer packs usually have a variety of curved tracks and with a little ingenuity it is usually possible to fit the curved tracks, or simply use a series of straight tracks laid at an angle to one another to build up the required bend in the track. A method I have found useful is to use rub-on transfers for pads and straight pieces of track, but to use a printed circuit pen to fill in any awkward pieces of curved track. This method is very quick and simple, but can provide very neat results provided adequate care is taken. In fact quite good results can be obtained using rub-down transfers for the pads and a printed circuit resist pen to add in all the tracks.

When laying down the tracks be careful not to take the tracks so far onto the pads that the holes in the pad centres are covered over. Due to these holes the copper at the centre of the pads is etched away during the etching process, and this leaves little indentations in the pads which guide the drill bit accurately into position when the component mounting holes are drilled. This gives excellent accuracy when drilling the mounting holes for dual-in-line (DIL) integrated circuits, since the mounting holes are drilled with an accuracy virtually equal to that of the rub-on transfers. Using the first method of printed circuit production described in this book the accuracy of the component mounting hole positioning might not be all it could be unless you are very careful indeed, and any shortfall in accuracy tends to be most noticeable on DIL integrated circuit clusters. With so many electronic projects being based on DIL integrated circuits these days it is well worthwhile considering the use of rub-on transfers (or a mixture of rub-on transfers and a resist pen) in order to obtain really neat and professional looking results. This method may be a little more time consuming and expensive, but the added time and expense will probably be reflected in the finished board.

Of course, you must also be careful not to leave tracks falling fractionally short of pads, but if this should occur it is not necessary to completely relay the track, and there should be no difficulty in neatly bridging the gap with a small piece of rub-on track. Probably the best method of laying the tracks is to first place the sheet of transfers over the board with one of the rub-on tracks in the correct position so that the length of track required can be marked on the sheet. This piece of track is then carefully cut out using either a small pair of scissors or a modelling knife, accurately repositioned on the board, and rubbed-down onto the board.


**Track Mounted Components**

Although conventionally a printed circuit board has the copper tracks and pads on the underside with the components mounted on the top side of the board, there is an alternative type of board which has both the copper tracks and pads, and the components on the same side of the board. Normally this type of printed circuit board does not have any holes drilled in the board, and this makes construction of the board a little quicker and easier.

There are a few disadvantages to this system though, which is why most printed circuit boards are not of this type despite the simplicity of producing such boards. The main disadvantage is that of reduced physical strength. With a conventional printed circuit board the components are pressed down hard into place on one side of the board with the leadout wires soldered in place on the opposite side of the board, and the component mounting holes are only marginally larger than the leadout wires so that they also help to make the whole construction rigid and strong. Clearly this method of con-struction resists any upward, downward, or sideways pressure on components very effectively. In fact the components are

24

held in place much the same as if they were rivets!

With the components on the top side of the board together with the copper tracks and pads, any sideways or upwards pressure on components tends to pull the pads and tracks away from the board, and is likely to result in tracks becoming broken, apart from looking rather scrappy. In practice this is not likely to be a problem once the board has been completed and installed in the finished project, although in some cases there may be a danger of a loose component such as a battery coming into contact with the board and dislodging components. The main problem is when soldering components into place. The heat from the soldering iron tends to weaken the adhesive which bonds the copper to the base material of the printed circuit board, and just after a component has been soldered into place (and the joint has set but is still very hot) it can be very easy to rip the copper away from the base material. Just how much of a problem this is depends to some extent on the particular board used.

Apart from this difficulty I find it harder to solder the components in place due to the lack of component mounting holes to help keep components in place during the soldering operation, although this is something that no doubt becomes much easier with practice. A third and minor drawback is merely that this type of printed circuit board perhaps looks a little less neat and professional than a conventional board.

Boards having the components and copper on the same side are produced using basically the same method as for conventional printed circuit boards, but obviously it is not essential to drill any component mounting holes in the board. An important point to bear in mind is that printed circuit track diagrams in magazines and books are normally for a conventional printed circuit board, and components such as integrated circuits will probably not fit onto this track pattern if they are placed on the track side of the board. You will find, for example, that whichever way round you place a DIL integrated circuit onto the track pattern the pins of the device do not match up with the right pads of the track pattern.

What is needed is a mirror image of the conventional track pattern, and it may be possible to see this pattern simply by holding the page carrying the design in front of a strong light and looking at the page from the wrong side so that (hopefully) you can see the pattern on the other side of the paper. This may not work due to printing of some kind on the opposite side of the page to the track pattern, but you can simply trace the pattern and then turn over the tracing to obtain the required design. These days the drawings of the component layouts for printed circuit boards often show the track pattern lightly shaded in, and this is of course the track pattern as it would be seen looking through the board from the component side, and is the track pattern needed for a board of this type.

## Printed Circuit Holders

Probably the most simple part of producing any printed circuit board is mounting and soldering the components in position. This merely entails fitting the components into place (making sure that they are inserted the right way round where appropriate), trimming off the leadout wires close to the underside of the board using a pair of wire cutters, and then finally soldering the leadout wires to the copper pads. This can be a little awkward in practice since ideally you need three hands: one to hold the soldering iron, one to hold the solder, and the third one to hold the board and component. A useful way around this problem is to place the reel of solder on the bench with a few inches of solder protruding over the edge of the workbench. Taking the soldering iron in one hand and the printed circuit board and component in the other, the soldered joints are made by taking the iron and the board/ component to the solder, rather than the solder and iron to the board/component. This may prove to be a little difficult at first, but after a little practice it is very easy to produce good soldered joints using this method. Incidentally, this system works well with both conventional printed circuit boards and the type where the components are fitted on the copper side of the board.

Another method that can be used is to simply place the board component-side down on the bench so that the components are trapped in place between the board and the workbench, leaving both hands free to manipulate the solder and the soldering iron. However, you must insert and connect the small components such as resistors first, gradually working up to the largest components such as high value electrolytics, otherwise the components will not be held close against the board. It is not advisable to have a significant gap between the body of a component and the board since this is physically weak with any downwards pressure on the component tending push down on the pads and tracks, possibly tearing them away from the rest of the board and producing broken tracks.

A similar technique is to use something like Bostik Blue Tak or plasticine to hold the components which can be connected in any desired order, although it will still probably be easiest if the smallest components are wired in place first.

An idea which is similar in principle, but much more sophisticated, is a printed circuit construction frame, and commercially produced units of this type are available from a few of the larger electronic component retailers. The basic idea is to first fit all the components in place on the board, and then the board is clamped into a frame. A pad of soft foam material is then clamped in place over the component side of the board so that it can be turned over without any of the components falling out of place. The leadout wires are then trimmed to length and the soldered joints completed with the frame not only holding the components in place, but adding extra weight to the assembly so that it does not tend to slide around on the workbench while the connections are being made.

A frame of this type is a very useful tool if you are likely to build a substantial number of boards over a period of time, but the expense could probably not be justified if only the occasional small printed circuit board is to be constructed. With a little ingenuity it should be possible to build ones own printed circuit construction frame without too much difficulty. In order to obtain the best results with a construction frame it is usually necessary to add any really large components such as transformers or very high value electrolytics after the small and medium sized components have been soldered into circuit.

Aerosol sprays for coating finished printed circuit boards are available, and these differ from flux lacquers in that they are simply designed to give a protective coating to the board and not to aid good soldered joints. Thus they are used to coat the board once the components have been soldered in place rather than before. Unless a project is going to be used under adverse conditions it is by no means essential to use any protective coating on the board.

## Chapter 2

## PHOTOGRAPHIC METHODS

Printed circuit boards, whether of your own design or copied from a book or magazine, can be produced using a simple photographic technique to obtain a board having the etch resist in the required pattern. Producing a printed circuit board photographically only differs from the simple methods of board production described in Chapter 1 in the way in which the resist is applied to the board and the required pattern is obtained, and in other respects board construction is exactly the same.

The basic technique is to first obtain a photographic positive, then expose a photosensitive board to ultraviolet light through the positive, and finally to develop the board so that the exposed photo-resist is removed and the required track pattern is left. The board is then etched, drilled, and completed in the normal way.

While it must be admitted that this system of board production is more expensive than the simple methods described in Chapter 1 of this book, it does allow really good results to be obtained. Boards equal in quality to professionally made boards can be produced, although the cost of producing the board may actually be comparable to that of a ready-made board. This obviously depends on the cost of the materials used and the cost of a ready made board, but even if there is little or no monetary saving obtained by making a board using this method it is something that I would still recommend. Producing top quality printed circuit boards using this photographic method is a very interesting and rewarding task, and should not merely be regarded as a chore which must be done in order to obtain a good quality board. It is certainly more satisfying and a greater achievement to produce a good quality finished article using a home-constructed board than it is using a ready-made one.

An advantage of this method of board production is that modern, highly intricate printed circuit boards can be produced without too much difficulty, whereas some modern home-constructor printed circuit designs are verging on the impossible using the techniques described in Chapter 1. It is very quick and simple to produce a number of identical boards using this system, and this is useful if you wish to build two or three examples of a project for some reason, or where a project uses several identical circuit boards.

This system is also very useful if you are designing and building your own printed circuit boards since you can draw the printed circuit track design on translucent drafting film, and then this actual size drawing can be used as the photographic positive to produce the board. In this chapter we will only deal with producing a photographic positive from a design in a book or magazine, and notes on designing and drafting your own printed circuit layouts will be covered in the next chapter of this book.


## Making A Positive

At the time of writing all the photo-resists available to the amateur user would seem to be of the positive variety, and the sensitised board must therefore be exposed through a photographic positive of the track design. In other words the film or drawing from which the board is made must be transparent or translucent where there are to be areas of plain board, and opaque where there are to be copper tracks. Thus, when the board is exposed through the positive the areas where the resist is to remain are shielded, and the areas where the resist is to be removed are exposed to the ultraviolet light source. When the board is immersed in the developer the exposed areas of resist dissolve and the remaining unexposed areas of resist form the required copper track pattern.

Unfortunately it is not possible to simply cut out the copper track pattern from a magazine or book and use this drawing as the photographic positive. Apart from problems with any printing on the reverse side of the drawing, the paper would tend to seriously impede the exposure of the plain areas of board while the inked areas of the drawing would provide only a slightly more difficult path for the ultraviolet light. Therefore it is necessary to transfer the design in the book or magazine onto a sheet of translucent polyester film or some similar material, with the areas or copper track being marked by a reasonably opaque material of some kind.

There are two basic ways of producing a suitable photographic positive, and one of these is to use a photographic process of some kind. The other is to simply copy the design onto drafting film using rub-on transfers, die-cut drafting tapes and symbols, or something of this nature.

If we take the photographic processes first; by far the most simple and quick means of obtaining a positive is to use a photocopying machine. However, this is only possible using a plain paper photocopier that uses dry toner powder, which gives an accurate one-to-one copy, and can take a transparent or translucent drafting film instead of ordinary paper. The quality of the copy obtained depends to some extent on the quality of the copier used, but using a good quality machine it is possible to obtain excellent results very rapidly with a minimum of fuss and bother.

An alternative system which is much slower and a little more difficult is to use a positive copying film. This is probably a more practical method since most constructors will almost certainly not have access to a suitable photocopier to permit the simple method described above to be used. I have produced positives using this method, and I used a special kit of tools and materials (the Electrolube CM100 Circuit Maker Kit). To the best of my knowledge, and at the time of writing, the special materials required are only available to amateur users in this kit, or as top-up kits of materials for this kit.

The CM100 kit is supplied with a detailed instruction manual, and here we will only consider the basic procedure used to obtain a finished photographic positive. The first step is to expose the positive film, and this entails placing the design to be copied and the film in a special frame provided with the kit, the main purpose of this frame is to hold the film and the drawing in good contact. The drawing is placed in the frame first, and then the film is placed with its sensitive surface facing downwards towards the drawing. The two are firmly trapped between a piece of foam material (below the drawing) and a sheet of glass (above the film), and the film is exposed using a powerful electric lamp positioned about 2 feet above the film. The length of the exposure is determined by making a test strip before going on to make a full copy of the board.

Because the film is exposed by light which travels through the film and is then reflected back up from the drawing, and not by light which travels through the drawing and onto the film, there does not seem to be much of a problem with printing on the opposite side of the page to the drawing producing an image on the film. However, if a problem of this type does arise a simple solution is to place a piece of black paper or card beneath the drawing, and it is probably as well to always do this so that film is not unnecessarily wasted. The film is not very sensitive incidentally, and this has the big advantage of enabling it to be handled in subdued light without fogging occuring, with no photographic safelight being needed.

The film is processed in a two-part developer, rinsed, and then fixed. This leaves a positive which has transparent areas that tend to be rather less transparent than would be ideal, but a clearing solution can be used to rectify this problem. The final stage is to wash the film and hang it up to dry.

Incidentally, the CM100 kit contains most of the items needed to produce the finished board from the photographic positive, and is not just a kit for producing positives from drawings.

There is a similar method of obtaining a positive, although I have not had first hand experience of this one. This system involves first making a paper negative using a similar arrangement to that described above, with the sensitive surface of the negative paper placed down onto the drawing, and the light source shining down through the paper and onto the drawing. A transparent positive is then made from the negative by having the positive film with its sensitive side facing upwards, placing the negative paper on top of the positive paper with the negative image facing downwards, and then exposing the positive to light shone through the negative paper.

This system obviously involves an extra stage, and the films must be handled in total darkness or under a red photographic safelight. The materials involved are quite inexpensive though.

## Tracing Designs

Photographic methods of obtaining a positive have the advantage of enabling complex boards to be copied reasonably quickly and with a high degree of accuracy. Tracing a printed circuit design onto drafting film using rub-on transfers or other drafting aids is likely to be a somewhat time consuming job except when a very simple design is being copied. Despite this it is a good method that can provide good results provided reasonable care is taken, and no doubt many constructors find that tracing a design is more interesting than the photographic copying methods.

Tracing a positive is quite easy and is similar to using rub-on transfers as the etch resist on the board, but it is somewhat more straight forward than copying the design onto the board. Basically all you have to do is to place a piece of translucent or transparent drafting film over the drawing to be copied, and then use the transfers to accurately copy the design which will clearly show through the drafting film. In order to obtain accurate results it is essential to tape the drafting film to the drawing so that there is no risk of the tracing slipping out of position during its production. Ideally the drawing (or the entire page of the book or magazine) should be cut out and taped to a drawing board (which can simply be a piece of hardboard, thick perspex, or any other reasonably rigid board having a clean smooth surface). The drafting film can then be taped in place over the drawing, making sure that both are flat against the board.

A useful alternative to rub-down transfers are the die-cut symbols and tapes that are available from some of the larger electronic component retailers and a few suppliers who specialise in goods of this type. These are not intended for use as the resist for direct use on printed circuit board incidentally, and would probably not work well in this application. But for producing tracings and original artwork for use as photographic positives for the production of printed circuit boards they are very easy to use and give really excellent results.

Printed circuit pads are available in a wide range of sizes, but for producing actual size tracings or original artwork only the smaller sizes are really required. Pads 0.1 inches or 2.5mm in diameter are ideal for small components such as transistors, resistors, capacitors, etc., although it will be necessary to use smaller types around 2mm in diameter at places where the pads are very closely spaced. Larger pads of about 3mm in diameter are useful for larger components such as preset resistors, or for marking the positions of the board's mounting holes. Pads normally have a hole at the centre, and if there is a choice of diameter for this hole it is best to choose a small diameter as this tends to aid good accuracy when the component mounting holes are drilled on the finished board. Also, having large holes in the pads tends to make it more difficult to produce good soldered joints when fitting the components onto the finished board.

While the pads for DIL integrated circuits could be lines of individual pads, it is more convenient to use the DIL clusters that are available, and these will also give superior accuracy and neater results. The single pads are usually on rolls of paper with a clear adhesive tape being used to hold them in position on the roll. However, the tape only covers half of each pad (as shown in Figure 6(a)) so that by holding the uncovered part of the pad against the roll of paper it is possible to peel away the tape without pulling the pad from the paper. With the tape removed the pads can then be easily prised away from the paper backing and placed on the tracing. A pointed knife or tweezers are ideal for moving the pads from the roll to the tracing. An advantage of die-cut symbols over rub-down transfers is that the die-cut symbols can easily be lifted up from the tracing and repositioned if necessary, and the self adhesive backing does not seem to significantly deteriorate even if the pads are repositioned several times. On the other hand, accurately positioning die-cut pads is perhaps a little more tricky than positioning rub-on transfers. Incidentally, die-cut pads are sometimes supplied on two-part cards (as shown in Figure 6(b)). Here the pads are removed by first tearing the two halves of the card apart so that the pads are left on one section, and are then easily removed from that section.

Integrated circuit clusters are rather different in that they are marked in ink on a thin transparent plastic film which is

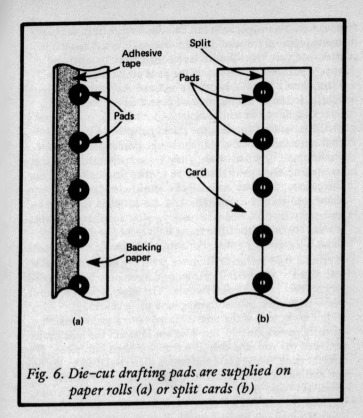

*Fig. 6. Die–cut drafting pads are supplied on paper rolls (a) or split cards (b)*

self adhesive on the underside, and is fitted onto a paper backing. In use a DIL cluster is torn away from the others in the strip, and the backing paper is usually in two halves so that initially only one half has to be removed. This is very useful as it enables the cluster to be slid around on the drafting film until it is accurately in position, and then the uncovered half is pressed down onto the drafting film to fix the cluster in place. The remaining backing paper is removed so that the rest of the cluster can be pressed down into place. It should perhaps be pointed out that the die-cut pads on cards can be positioned and fixed in place in much the same way if desired. Also, the die-cut pads on paper rolls can be pulled away from the paper backing tape, positioned over the tracing, pressed down into place, and then the adhesive tape pulled away to leave the symbol in position. However, the pads used for actual size tracings and original artwork are so small that it is probably more practical to use the method described earlier which in practice tends to be a little easier.

The tapes used to mark the tracks between pads are somewhat reminiscent of the old fabric type insulation tapes, but much thinner and narrower. They are actually made of a crepe material which enables them to be formed into quite tight curves if necessary, and they can easily be joined at a sharp angle where really tight turns are required. Like die-cut pads, they can be repeatedly repositioned if necessary. Most suppliers sell tapes in a variety of widths from about 0.03 inches or 0.8 mm to about 0.2 inches or 5mm. For actual size drawings tape widths of around 0.04 inches or 1mm are generally the most suitable, with tapes of around 0.03 inches or 0.8mm only being needed for compact and complex layouts. The larger tapes are useful where large areas of the drawing have to be covered.

In use the end of the tape is placed onto a pad so that it partially covers the pad, but does not obstruct the hole in the centre of the pad, and then it is firmly pressed into place. If a straight track is being laid the tape is then stretched to the next pad and pressed into position, and then the tape is firmly pressed in place along its length. It is then cut to length using a very sharp knife or a scalpel, the blade used must be very sharp if a neat cut is to be made. It must also be treated with due care. When making the cut, angle the blade slightly towards the edge of the pad. If the blade does then accidentally cut through the pad, the end of the tape should help to cover the damage. Very fine cuts in tracks or pads will probably be of no practical importance as they are unlikely to be reproduced on the finished board, but they should obviously be avoided if possible.

If a pad should become badly damaged then it should obviously be replaced. Integrated circuit pads are more easily damaged than individual pads, and when laying track between an integrated circuit pad and an ordinary one it is advisable to start at the integrated circuit pad. The tape is then cut to length at the other pad which is less vulnerable to damage. When laying tapes between integrated circuit pads either extra care should be taken when cutting the tapes, or the tape can be cut with a small pair of scissors and pressed down into place. With this second method it is necessary to accurately judge the correct position for the cut or the tape will either fall short of the pad or cover over the hole at the centre of the pad, but a little practice is all that is needed. A third method is to cut the tape well short of the integrated circuit pad, and then lay a bridging piece of tape in place from the pad to the first piece of tape, overlapping the two pieces of tape slightly.

The narrow tapes used in actual size drawings can be worked around curves without too much difficulty, but avoid getting kinks in the tape, and try to get smooth steady curves. Remember that the tape can simply be pulled up and relayed if necessary, and that this can be repeated a number of times until the required curve is produced.

You may find it difficult to obtain integrated circuit DIL clusters in anything other than 16 pin clusters, but these are easily cut down to 14 or 8 pin sets with the aid or a ruler and a scalpel or very sharp knife. Large clusters such as 18 and 20 pin types can also be built up, although this is a little tricky and care should be taken to ensure good accuracy.

It is quite feasable to use a variety of drafting aids to complete the tracing, and a mixture of rub-on transfers, die-cut symbols and tapes, and drawing ink could be used. However, in general it is best not to use a mixture of materials since practical difficulties can arise. For example, using rub-on pads with drafting tapes can be awkward with the pads being relatively easy to damage when cutting tapes, and if a tape is pulled away from the drawing it is quite likely to take part of a pad with it. If ink is used to complete all or part of the tracing it is essential to use a good quality black drawing ink which is opaque, and drawings made using fibre tip pens or pencils are unlikely to give usable results. In fact they would probably fail totally.

The most readily available drafting film is a polyester type which has a mat finish on both sides, and this accepts drawing ink, rub-on transfers, and die-cut symbols/tapes without any difficulty. This material also has good resistance against warping and stretching, and is ideal for this application. However, other materials such as clear or semi-mat acetate sheets seem to give perfectly satisfactory results when used in conjunction with rub-on transfers or die-cut symbols and tapes.

## Sensitised Board

Having obtained the positive of the track design the next step in the process is to obtain a sensitised board of the correct size. The corners of the board are normally marked on the drawing in the book or magazine by a couple of short lines at right angles to each other, and these are measured to determine the size of the board if this is not specified on the drawing or in the accompanying text. Note that the insides of the corner markers correspond with the outside edges of the board, and you should therefore measure the distances between the insides of the corner marker lines not the outsides. With many designs these days it is essential to cut the board to size accurately. For example, with many projects the finished printed circuit board slots into guide rails inside the case, and if the board is marginally over-size it will not fit into place, or if it is slightly under-size it may simply fall out of the rails and will not be held in place properly. Incidentally, if you are tracing the design to produce a positive, be sure to include the corner markers as these are needed to align the drawing and the board accurately before making the exposure.

If you use a board which is ready-coated with ultraviolet photo-resist the board should be handled under subdued lighting conditions, and should not be exposed to bright daylight. The board should also be stored under dark conditions. There is a significant amount of ultraviolet light in ordinary daylight, and bright sunlight will usually have quite a strong ultraviolet content. The light output from artificial (tungsten) lighting is very different, and is largely at the red end of the light spectrum. Consequently ultraviolet photo-resists are insensitive to tungsten lighting, although prolonged exposure to this type of lighting should still be avoided. Some ready-coated boards are supplied with a black plastic film over the resist, and these are less prone to fogging by ambient light. When cutting a ready-coated board to size be very careful not to damage the coating of resist. These resists are usually quite tough, but can easily be chipped or scratched away if you are a bit careless with sharp tools. Another advantage of the boards that have a plastic protective coating is that they are less prone to physical damage.

Photo-resists for use on ordinary copper laminate board are available, and these do have a couple of advantages over ready-coated boards. The more obvious advantage is the saving in cost obtained. Ready-coated boards seem to cost about twice as much as uncoated boards, but the cost of coating a board with photo-resist yourself is likely to be no more than a few pence. Thus ready-coated boards are just about twice as expensive as boards which are coated by the constructor. The less obvious advantage, but one which I would consider to be at least as important, is that if something should go wrong during exposure or development with a home-coated board it is merely necessary to recoat the board and start again. All that will have been lost is a few pence worth of photo-resist and some time. With a ready-coated board the cost of the ruined resist will have been relatively high, and unless you have some photo-resist so that the board can be reused, the board itself will be wasted as well.

Ready-coated boards do have advantages in that they should have a really good even coating of resist, and should therefore give superb final results. They also enable the finished board to be produced more rapidly with a minimum of fuss and mess. Which you choose really depends on whether you consider the extra cost of ready-coated boards to be justified by their greater convenience, and possibly by the quality of results obtained compared to using home-coated boards.

## Coating A Board

To the best of the author's knowledge, at the time of writing the only photo-resist available that is painted onto the board with a brush or similar applicator is the type supplied with the CM100 Circuit Maker kit (which was mentioned earlier), and one of the CM100 replenishment kits. I have not found it too easy to obtain a really even coating of resist using this particular type, although the same is also true of other photo-resists I have tried. Before applying any resist the board should be cleaned and polished to a really good finish, and it should be thoroughly dried. If the board is not properly cleaned and dried it may be impossible to get a good even coating of resist, and the board may not etch properly either. A resist applicator is supplied with the CM100 kit, but better results may be obtained using a soft brush. This can be stroked down the length of the board to produce a coating of consistent thickness. A blower brush of the type used to clean cameras and lenses seems to be ideal for this.

With any photo-resist it is essential to have a coating of the correct thickness. If too little resist is applied to the board it will probably be fairly obvious since areas of the board will have a noticeably thin coating, or even no perceptible coating at all. When such a board is developed there are inevitably pads and lengths of track that are absent. If the board is coated too thickly it will be difficult or impossible to produce a reasonably even coating, with the resist tending to build up around the edges of the board, and perhaps forming into ridges elsewhere on the board. With a heavy coating of resist it may be impossible to dissolve all the unwanted areas of resist at the development stage, especially around the edges of the board or other places where very thick ridges of resist have formed.

There is then a good reason for trying to obtain a coating of the correct thickness, and of a consistent thickness, and it is not just a matter of aesthetics. It is not necessary to have a perfect coating on the board in order to obtain satisfactory results, but the coating should have a reasonably plain appearance. It is of course possible to retouch parts of the developed board where tracks or pads have become indistinct, or to scrape away resist from what should be bare areas of board, but the quality of the finished board would probably suffer to some extent, and results obtained would probably not justify the time, effort, and expense put into the construction of the board. If the coating seems to be too thin, too thick, or lacking in consistency it is probably best to clean it all off, dry the board, and start again.

Remember that the resist is sensitive to daylight and must therefore be applied to the board somewhere that is shielded from daylight, but where there is still sufficient light to enable the board to be seen clearly. Once the resist has been applied successfully the board must be left to dry for at least an hour somewhere that is suitably dark, and preferably somewhere that will give some protection against dust falling onto the board. A few dust particles do not seem to matter too much and do not normally degrade the quality of the finished board significantly, but with a large amount of dust contaminating the coating of resist it is likely that the finished board will have a few broken or short circuited tracks. A cupboard should provide dark and fairly dust-free conditions and is probably the best place to leave the board to dry. The board should be in an almost perfectly horizontal position so that there is not a tendency for the resist to run to one end of the board and produce a very uneven coating.

## Spray Resists

Spray-on photo-resists are available, and "Postiv 20" seems to be the one which is most readily available (at the time of writing anyway). A lot of the notes given about brush-on resist apply also to spray-on resists, but the method of application is obviously totally different. The clean, dry board is sprayed with a conservative amount of resist from a distance of about 8 inches (200mm) and is immediately placed in a horizontal position and left to dry. Immediately after spraying the board a very blotchy and uneven coating of resist is likely to be obtained, but provided one part of the board has not been sprayed with a lot more resist (or less resist) than the rest of the board, and the board is quickly placed in an almost perfectly horizontal position, the resist will probably soon spread out over the board to produce a coating of consistent thickness. Note that the drying time for this resist is at least 24 hours at normal room temperatures. Do not be tempted to shorten resist drying times even if the resist does seem to have fully dried, otherwise you may well find that some of the resist sticks to the positive when the board and the positive are separated after the exposure has been made.

If the photo-resist seems reluctant to spread reasonably evenly over the board this might just be due to the board being inadequately cleaned and (or) dried. Should the board appear to be perfectly clean and dry and the resist will still not flow over the board, try spraying a small amount of resist onto the middle of the board and then smearing this thinly over the entire board. If the board is then resprayed a reasonably even coating should be obtained. Be careful to avoid getting dust particles from the paper onto the board, and gently wipe away any particles that are left on the board before applying the main coating of resist.

The drying time for the "Postiv 20" spray can be greatly reduced by heating up the board, and it can in fact be reduced to only about 15 to 20 minutes. Ideally an infra-red oven or drying cabinet should be used, but it is unlikely that many amateur users will have access to such equipment. The fumes given off by the resist during drying do not seem to be particularly inflammable or explosive, and I have had no problems drying boards in an ordinary oven set for the lowest possible temperature (with any food or cooking utensils removed from the oven). This method also provides a dark and fairly dust-free environment. It would probably be possible to heat the board using a radiant electric fire or by placing it on a radiator, but obviously it would be better to simply leave the board for 24 hours rather than rig up some method of drying the board that could be a dangerous fire hazard. If you do use heat to reduce the drying time make sure that the board is not taken above about 70 degrees Centigrade or it could be damaged. the ideal drying temperature is between 60 and 70 degrees Centigrade.

## Condensation

On cold wet days it may be found that the photo-resist will not spread evenly over the board, or having done so it then tends to form in patches, or a translucent film appears over parts of the board. This is caused by condensation on the board, and a board which has been affected in this way will not be usable. If heat is being used to dry the board the simple way of avoiding condensation is to warm the board before applying the photo-resist, and to place the board into the drying oven as soon as the resist has been placed on the board.

If the resist is simply going to be left to dry naturally, warming the board before applying the resist should help, but may not be the complete answer to the problem. Keeping the board slightly warm or even raising the room temperature slightly should completely eliminate the problem though.

## Exposure

Having by some means or other obtained a properly coated board of the correct size it is then necessary to make the exposure. This can be done without the use of any special equipment, but results may be rather inconsistent. Without an ultraviolet light source of some kind ordinary daylight, and preferably direct sunlight, can be used as the light source.

The basic procedure is quite simple and consists of placing the board in a horizontal position with the sensitive surface facing upwards, with the positive placed accurately in position on top of the board. The positive must have the "component side" facing down onto the board and the "track side" facing upwards, otherwise a mirror image of the required track pattern will be produced. Always double check this point before making an exposure. In order to obtain good results it is essential that the board and the positive are in contact over their entire surfaces, and it is unlikely that the positive will naturally lay perfectly flat against the board. Even quite small gaps between the positive and the board could result in tracks and pads being reduced in size on the finished board, or even failing to appear altogether! A sheet of good quality (flat) glass is therefore placed on top of the positive to hold it flat against the board. This general arrangement is illustrated in Figure 7. Incidentally, when using the "CM 100 Circuit Maker" kit the frame used during the production of the positive can also be used during the exposure of the board.

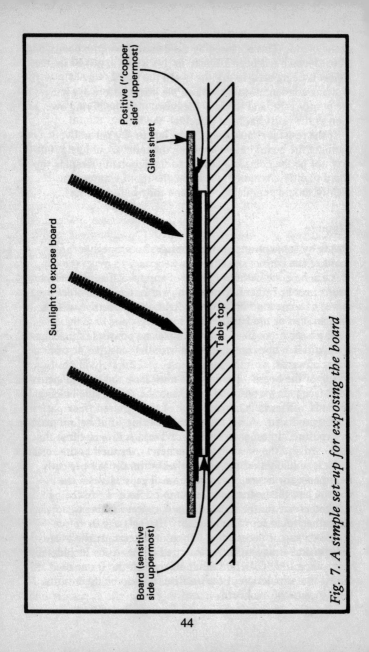

Sunlight to expose board

Positive ("copper side" uppermost)

Glass sheet

Table top

Board (sensitive side uppermost)

*Fig. 7. A simple set-up for exposing the board*

The use of plastic instead of glass is not recommended since many transparent plastic sheets are relatively light and far from perfectly flat, and might fail to keep the board and the positive in good contact. Many clear plastics also tend to have an ultraviolet filtering effect, and would greatly increase the exposure time required. Glass does reduce the amount of ultraviolet light reaching the board significantly, but the increase in exposure time this causes is not large enough to be a problem. If the sheet of glass has sharp edges (which it almost certainly will) these can be smoothed on an oilstone, or covered with insulation tape, so that they are rendered harmless.

Of course, the board should be shielded from light as best as possible while it is being set up for the exposure as the photo-resist might otherwise become fogged. The equipment should also be set up for the exposure as quickly as possible to minimise the risk of fogging.

The exposure time depends on a number of factors. Some photo-resists are more sensitive than others and therefore require less exposure time. The base material of the positive will also have an effect on the exposure time since some base materials block a significant amount of ultraviolet light while others have a very high level of ultraviolet transmission. These factors are not too important since the differences are only likely to be relatively minor, and provided you always use the same materials when producing boards the same exposure time will always be needed for a given light level.

The weakness of this very simple method of board production is that the light level used during exposure will vary quite considerably from one time to the next. At mid-day on a clear day in the middle of summer the light level could be high enough to produce an exposure time of only about 5 minutes or even less, whereas a heavily overcast afternoon in the middle of winter might produce such a low light level that correct exposure would be impossible.

This makes it necessary to make a few tests using odd scraps of sensitised board to determine the correct exposure time each time a board is made, and assuming the light level remains fairly constant it should then be possible to obtain reliable results. It would probably be worthwhile noting down the exposure time

45

and the weather conditions at the time (including an exposure reading taken using an exposure meter or suitably equipped camera if possible), and using this information it might then be possible to predict the correct exposure time accurately on some future occasion. This should certainly be possible once a reasonably long list of light levels and corresponding exposure times has been built up.

An alternative to daylight is to use the ultraviolet light from a "sunray" lamp, and the big advantage of this system is that once the correct exposure has been determined this will remain the same on future occasions provided exactly the same set-up and materials are used. This can avoid much wasted time and materials, especially when making the first few printed circuit boards.

The arrangement employed must obviously be designed to suit the particular type of "sunray" lamp in use. It might be necessary to have the board positioned vertically, and some means of clamping the positive and board between the glass and some form of backing board will then have to be devised.

In order to obtain a reasonably short exposure time it will almost certainly be necessary to have the board positioned quite close to the ultraviolet source, but do not position it so close that an uneven exposure over the coating of resist is produced. Measure the distance from the lamp to the board that is eventually used, and always use exactly the same distance when making boards on subsequent occasions. Some ultraviolet lamps can only provide the ultraviolet light in conjunction with infra-red radiation (heat). With such lamps the minimum distance that can be used is likely to be the smallest distance that does not cause the board to become excessively hot.

It is important to bear in mind that ultraviolet light is dangerous, and apart from the obvious danger of sunburn it can be harmful to ones eyes. The appropriate type of goggles can be worn, or you can simply leave the room while the exposure is in progress (making sure that any other people or pets also leave). The "sunray" lamp will probably have an instruction booklet or label which details the necessary safety precautions, incidentally.

## Exposure Box

The most convenient and reliable way of exposing the board is to use one of the ultraviolet exposure boxes that are produced specifically for this purpose. Some of these are quite large units having powerful ultraviolet lamps that give very short exposure times, but these are quite expensive and probably not a practical proposition for amateur users. However, there are smaller units available which normally have a couple of 12 inch 8 watt fluorescent ultraviolet tubes which give an exposure time of around 5 to 25 minutes, and can take boards of up to about 250 by 150mm or so in size. These are very much less expensive and should prove to be perfectly adequate for normal amateur requirements.

Figure 8 shows the basic arrangement used in an exposure box of this type. The ultraviolet tubes are mounted at the bottom of the box with a sheet of glass mounted towards the top of the box. The positive is placed on the glass and taped in position with the "copper side" facing downwards towards the glass and tubes and the "component side" uppermost. The board is then placed accurately in position over the positive, again with the copper side facing downwards, and again it is taped in position. A piece of foam material in the lid of the box presses the board and the positive together when the lid of the box is closed, and ensures that the two are in good contact with one another. The board and the positive are taped in position to make sure that they are not pushed out of alignment as the lid of the case is closed. The exposure box should not be used with the lid raised as this would allow the ultraviolet light to escape from the unit (which could be hazardous) and the board would not be pressed down onto the positive.

It would probably be possible to home-construct an ultraviolet exposure box without too much difficulty since it is basically quite a simple piece of equipment. However, the saving in cost over a ready-made unit might not be very great.

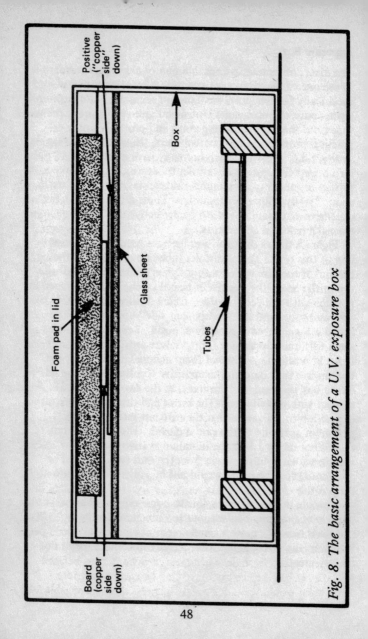

Fig. 8. The basic arrangement of a U.V. exposure box

# Development

All the ready-coated boards and photo-resists I have ever
encountered have been designed for development in a weak
solution of caustic soda (sodium hydroxide), although there
may well be boards or resists which require a different chemical
for development. Assuming that you use a board or resist
intended for development in a standard caustic soda developer,
it is a solution having 7 grams of caustic soda to one litre of
water that is required.

Caustic soda, as its name implies, is a highly caustic substance
and it is advisable not to handle crystals of this chemical. Once
in a weak solution it is not so dangerous, but it is still advisable
to avoid contact with this chemical and to wash off any that
should get onto the skin. It might be possible to obtain this
from a local chemists shop, and it should certainly be available
from a large chemists or a photographic shop that sells "raw"
photographic chemicals. Caustic soda crystals are not very
expensive, and because such a weak solution is used the
developer is very inexpensive.

It is essential to make up a solution of the right strength since
the developer only needs to be slightly weak in order to almost
totally block development. If the solution is slightly over-
strength it is likely that the unexposed areas of photo-resist will
tend to dissolve almost as rapidly as the exposed areas, resulting
in an inadequate coating of resist or no resist at all after
development. Even if an adequate coating of resist is left, it
could be softened and damaged during development so that it
is easily rubbed off, and could tend to wash away in the etching
solution.

It is advisable to make up a fairly large amount of developer
if possible since a comparatively large amount of caustic soda
crystals will then be needed, making it easier to measure out the
appropriate amount reasonably accurately. If only (say) 500ml
of developer is made up, just 3.5 grams of chemical would need
to be accurately measured. It would also be necessary to
frequently mix fresh developer as well since it must be used
once and then thrown away. Mixing up (say) two litres of
developer would give a better stock, and a more managable 14

grams of chemical would be required. A kitchen balance is good enough to weigh out the required amount of chemical sufficiently accurately, but this should be thoroughly washed immediately after it has been used. The crystals should readily dissolve in the water, but there is no violent reaction with heat being generated or anything like that.

Rather than mixing up large amounts of caustic soda solution you may prefer to make up a fairly small amount, say 250ml, but make it somewhat stronger than is required. A small amount of the over-strength solution can then be measured into the developing dish and diluted by the appropriate amount immediately prior to use. For example, if 14 grams of caustic soda crystals are mixed with 250ml of water, diluting this in the ratio of one part solution to seven parts water gives developer of the correct strength.

The developer should be placed in a small photographic dish or any similar flat dish, and it is only necessary to use sufficient to cover the board properly. With the board placed sensitive surface uppermost in the dish and a certain amount of agitation used to keep the developer flowing over the board the unwanted areas of resist should soon start to dissolve. It usually only takes about two to five minutes for all the unwanted resist to dissolve. With some resists it is helpful to use a small swab of cottonwool to clear away resist which has softened but is reluctant to dissolve in the developer. Remove the board from the developer and thoroughly rinse it as soon as development has been completed or the wanted areas of resist might start to soften or dissolve. The board is then ready for immediate etching in the normal way, after which the drilling is completed and the components are soldered into place.

Assuming the developer has been mixed accurately at the right strength, if the board will not develop properly it almost certainly means that it has been under or over exposed. A lack of exposure results in the developer having little effect on the board, and over exposure causes the unwanted areas of resist to rapidly dissolve with the wanted areas being dissolved to some extent as well. Usually this just results in a narrowing of tracks and shrinking of pads, but in an extreme case it might result in virtually all the resist being dissolved. Incidentally, after exposure it will probably be possible to see a faint image of the track pattern on the photo-resist coating. A lack of this image almost certainly indicates under exposure while a very strong image is probably indicative of over exposure.

If trying a variety of exposure times fails to give satisfactory results the most likely cause of the problem is that the developer is seriously over or under strength.

Before etching the board it is advisable to carefully examine it to ensure that no small unwanted areas of resist remain or small parts of the track pattern are missing. Any small pieces of unwanted resist can easily be scraped away using a small pen knife, and it is much easier to remove the resist than to remove pieces of copper from the finished board. A printed circuit resist pen can be used to carefully fill in any small areas of resist that are damaged. However, if the coating, exposure, and development stages are carried out properly there should be no need to remove or add any resist to the board prior to etching.

An exception to this is where there are extremely narrow tracks on the board, particularly where tracks run between integrated circuit pads. During exposure the ultraviolet light tends to penetrate under the dark areas of the positive at the very edges. This can produce a very slight narrowing of tracks and shrinkage of pads on the finished board, although this may be too slight to be noticeable in many cases. Where tracks are exceedingly narrow to start with, this slight undercutting can produce a serious narrowing of the tracks. If this should occur it is advisable to use a resist pen to just slightly widen out these tracks again to make quite sure that they provide a good low resistance path on the finished board.

One final point is that although, as mentioned earlier, used developer should not be stored for future use but should be thrown away, it is quite acceptable to develop two or three boards in the same dish of developer provided they are either developed simultaneously or in rapid succession. Do not try to process a large number of boards in a small amount of developer in case the developer becomes exhausted and one or more boards become ruined.

## Double Sided Boards

Double sided printed circuit boards can be a little difficult to build, and it would be advisable to gain some experience constructing single sided boards before progressing to these. Most home-constructor projects only seem to require a single sided board, but the number of double sided designs published does seem to be increasing, and having the ability to produce this type of board is probably a well worthwhile skill. Commercially produced double sided boards are produced photographically from a single drawing which has tracks on one side of the board represented by blue transparent drafting tape, and the tracks on the opposite side represented by red transparent tape. A filtering process is then used during exposure to effectively eliminate one or other of the coloured tapes so that only the tracks for one side of the board are produced when each side of the board is exposed. Thus, provided the process is carried out properly, only the correct track pattern appears on each side of the board, and as both are produced from the same drawing excellent accuracy is obtained with no mismatch between the two sides of the board. Unfortunately this type of process is not really a practical proposition for amateur constructors, and a more simple method must be used.

The following system is quite simple and straight forward, and can be used with any of the methods of board production described in this book (i.e. resist pen, resist transfers, or photo-resist), and gives excellent results.

Initially what will be the component side of the board is covered over with resist, paint, or any similar substance that will protect the copper coating on this side of the board from the etchant. The copper tracks on the underside of the board are then produced using whatever system you normally use for printed circuit production, and all the holes are drilled in the board. Next the resist is removed from the component side of the board but the underside of the board is covered with resist. The track pattern on the component side of the board is then produced in the normal way, and as the holes are already in the board there should be no problems with the top and bottom sides of the board being out of alignment, especially if a resist pen or resist transfers are being used. If photo-resist is the method used it is obviously necessary to carefully align the positive with the holes in the board. Finally, the resist is removed from both sides of the board, and the through-pins and components are soldered into place.

With some double sided printed circuit boards the copper laminate on the component side of the board does not carry any interconnections, but is simply connected to the earthed supply rail and acts as a screen. With this type of board the underside can be produced in the manner described above. However, instead of then removing all the resist from the component side of the board it is merely necessary to remove the resist from around the component holes (which must be done in order to prevent short circuits through the copper earth plain). There should be no difficulty in removing this resist using a small twist drill. The board is then etched to remove the unwanted copper, but remember to protect the copper tracks on the underside of the board adequately so that they are not damaged during etching. It is possible to remove the unwanted copper on the component side of the board using a twist drill to partially drill into the board, but there is a danger of weakening the board, and this method is not recommended.

## Chapter 3

## DESIGNING PCBs

Designing printed circuit boards is not really very difficult
provided you start with fairly simple circuits and steadily
progress to more complex ones. While ideally you should try
to produce neat and professional looking boards, this is not
essential and provided the finished project works the printed
circuit design is perfectly acceptable. If you are only going to
use a simple method of board production, such as using an etch
resist pen, it might be better not to design boards to have a
highly compact layout with the components layed-out as neatly
as possible, and the connections to off-board components brought
out to convenient places at the edge of the board. This could
produce a highly intricate track pattern which would be
extremely difficult to produce using simple methods, and it
might be more convenient overall to use a relatively simple track
layout even if this will make the point-to-point wiring of the
project a little more difficult and less neat. In other words you
should design the board to suit the particular method of
construction that is to be used.

### Simple Boards

When drawing printed circuit designs it is much better to use
polyester drafting film (or a similar material) than paper, since
drafting film is translucent, and if the component layout and
track pattern are drawn on one side of the film, it is simply
turned over so that the proper track pattern can be seen (bearing
in mind that the track pattern drawn on the "component side"
of the film is a mirror image of the pattern that must be produced
on the finished board). It would be possible to draw the board
with both the component layout and the track pattern shown
together, and as viewed from the copper side of the board, but
this tends to be a little more awkward. Most people find it much
easier to think in terms of the board as viewed from the
component side, especially for components with several leadout

wires or pins such as integrated circuits or printed circuit mounting relays.

A drawing board of some kind is needed, but this can simply be a piece of hardboard or rigid plastic, or anything that is flat, rigid, and has a smooth surface. In order to make the drawing easy to see the board should have a white surface, but this can be achieved by simply taping a piece of white paper or card onto the board. Components such as integrated circuit, preset resistors, and relays must have the mounting holes in the board drilled with the correct spacing, and therefore drawn with the correct spacing on the design drawing. For example, DIL integrated circuits with up to 20 pins normally have pins spaced at 0.1 inch intervals with the rows of pins 0.3 inches apart. Obviously a ruler could be used in order to accurately draw the mounting holes for such components, but a much easier method is to use a precision backing grid. This is basically just a piece of polyester drafting film which normally has a mat finish on both sides, and one side has a grid of lines. In other words it is very much like graph paper but is drawn on drafting film rather than paper. Imperial grids having lines 0.1 inches apart are the most readily available type at the time of writing, and with so many electronic components having a pin spacing of 0.1 inches (or a multiple of 0.1 inches) these are probably the most convenient in use. Imperial grids having 0.05 inch spacing are also available, and are very useful when designing layouts actual size. Metric grids having 1mm or 2.5mm line spacing are produced, and these would aboviously be useful if you are using components which have metric pin spacing.

In use the grid is taped to the drawing board being careful to ensure that it lays flat against the board. The drafting film is then taped in place over the precision grid, again making sure that it is not buckled and that it lays flat against the board. The drawing can be made using a pencil, but note that you must either use a drafting film which is mat on both sides, or a film that has a mat finish on one side with this side uppermost. Transparent drafting film cannot be marked using a pencil.

## Example Design

As an example of how a simple printed circuit board can be designed we will take the circuit of Figure 9. This is a simple electronic doorbuzzer circuit, and it has been taken from the book BP80, "Popular Electronic Circuits Book 1" which is by the same publisher and author as this book. When designing a printed circuit board it is essential to be methodical if good, error free results are to be obtained. In this case the heart of the circuit is obviously integrated circuit IC1, and the obvious starting point is to draw this somewhere near the middle of the piece of drafting film. Most circuits are more complex than this one, and it is then a matter of taking one stage at a time, working methodically from one side of the circuit to the other. The technique is much the same as for a simple circuit such as the one shown in Figure 9, but instead of just one stage there are several which are taken in turn.

Returning to the circuit of Figure 9, having drawn in the integrated circuit the next step is to draw in the positive and negative supply rails, the negative rail a little way below the integrated circuit and the positive rail a little above it. The supply rails are then joined to the appropriate pins of IC1. There is no need to draw in the tracks properly as double lines to represent the extremities of the tracks, or as thick lines equal in thickness to the required track thickness. Neither is it necessary to draw in pads. Simply draw small dots to represent places where there are component mounting holes, and lines to show where copper tracks are required. It is not essential to draw in the components using a pencil of a different colour, but this will almost certainly make the drawing much clearer and help to prevent errors when the actual board is constructed. Components such as resistors, capacitors, and diodes can be represented by their circuit symbols, but with components such as integrated circuits or transistors it is probably better to use a rouch physical representation of the component (making it clear which way round it should be connected where appropriate). Component numbers can be added onto the drawing, but these are not strictly necessary, especially with simple designs, since reference to the circuit diagram should

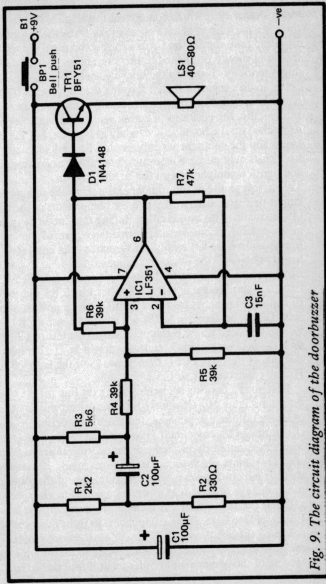

Fig. 9. The circuit diagram of the doorbuzzer

make it quite clear which component is which. If it is felt that there is a likelyhood of confusion arising when the components are fitted onto the finished board then component numbers should obviously be included. However, in some cases these might seriously clutter up the drawing, and it would then be better to do a separate sketch showing the component layout of the board and the component identification numbers. Incidentally, the positions of component mounting holes should be marked on the board as accurately as possible, but the copper tracks and the components only need to be marked roughly since their only purpose is to show you where to lay tracks and position components on the finished board.

It is best to add in the components near to the integrated circuit first, gradually working to the components at the edges of the circuit. This avoids either finding that too little space has been left for components, or that large parts of the finished board are left empty. If we start at the input (left hand) side of IC1 the obvious component to add in first is R5 from pin 3 of IC1 down to the negative supply rail, then C3 from IC1 pin 2 to the negative rail, after which R3 and R4 can be connected in series from pin 3 of IC1 to the positive supply. Next C2 can be drawn in to the left of these resistors, R1 and R2 can be added across the supply rails to the left of C2, and then the necessary copper tracks are drawn in. To complete this side of the design C1 is then drawn in to the left of R1 — R2 and connected across the supply rails.

This gives a drawing something along the lines of the one shown in Figure 10. Obviously there are a large number of ways of laying out the components, and there is no definitive printed circuit design for any circuit. Provided the finished project works the printed circuit design is successful. However, there are a few points which should be borne in mind. Remember that the circuit diagram gives you no real idea of the physical size and shape of the components represented by the symbols, and that this is an important factor when designing the board. It is helpful to have all the components in front of you when designing the board, especially any unusual components such as relays where it will probably be necessary to measure the pin spacing of the component in order to fit it into the design

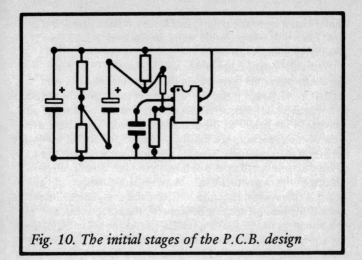

*Fig. 10. The initial stages of the P.C.B. design*

properly (some component catalogues give diagrams showing
the pin spacing of components and this should obviously be
used where possible). Provided you have access to the
components or sufficient physical data on them prior to
commencing work on the printed circuit design there is no real
excuse for accidentally leaving far too little or too much space
for a component. This is especially the case when designing
boards actual size so that no error of scale should be made. It
is best not to start designing a board until you do have all the
necessary physical data on the components used. This can save
a great deal of wasted time in redrawing designs to provide extra
space for components.

The printed circuit board can be layed out in much the same
way as the circuit diagram, but this is not likely to give the
neatest and most compact results, and in some cases would be
completely impractical. For example, C2 is shown horizontally
on the circuit diagram, but is fitted vertically into the printed
circuit design of Figure 10. Using an ordinary axial component
here fitted horizontally onto the board would almost certainly
result in a significant increase in the size of the finished board
and result in a lot of wasted space. Of course, if small size is not

of any importance the component layout is less critical, but in most cases you will probably want the finished unit to be reasonably compact.

Where the board must be as small as possible it may be helpful to use radial (printed circuit mounting) electrolytic capacitors, although it should be borne in mind that the reduction in board area that this permits is obtained at the expense of an increase in the height of the completed board. These days non-electrolytic capacitors are mostly of the printed circuit mounting type, and they normally have long leadout wires so that the printed circuit board does not have to use the same leadout spacing as the capacitors used. However, construction of the board is easier when it comes to fitting the components into place if the leadout spacing does match the component, and this also gives neater looking results. If, on the other hand, using the appropriate hole spacing in the board over-complicates the track pattern you may feel (with some justification) that using a wider spacing and a simpler track pattern is the more practical course of action. With polycarbonate and some other types of capacitor the leadout wires are very short, and there is a danger of the wires being pulled off the component if they are bent outwards to increase the effective leadout spacing. With components such as these it is virtually obligatory to use the appropriate hole spacing in the printed circuit board.

Resistors and axial capacitors can be mounted vertically on the board in order to save space if this would be more convenient for some reason. Where possible it is better to use proper vertical mounting capacitors since there are a couple of drawbacks to vertically mounting axial components. One is simply that there is a danger of the components being pushed down so that their leadout wires short circuit with each other. This possibility could be eliminated by using PVC insulating sleeving over the leadout wires, but it is much easier to use radial lead components. The second problem is that of reduced physical strength, with any downwards pressure on the components tending to tear at least one of the pads away from the board. There is no easy solution to this problem.

Printed circuit mounting resistors do not seem to be available to the amateur user, and if resistors must be fitted onto the board vertically there is no alternative to using ordinary types and accepting the resultant drawbacks. It is therefore advisable to use resistors mounted horizontally wherever possible. For ease of construction when fitting the components to the board, and in order to give neat results, it is a good idea to use a standard hole spacing for the resistors provided this will not give any real difficulties with the printed circuit track design. For ordinary miniature (third or quarter watt) resistors 0.4 inch hole spacing is ideal.

If we now complete the printed circuit design, R6 and R7 are the logical choices for the next components to be added to the design. Adding R6 is quite straight forward since this can be positioned to the side of and below IC1, with its lower end connected to pin 3 of IC1 via a short track taken between pins 4 and 5 of the integrated circuit. The upper end of R6 just connects straight across to pin 6 of the integrated circuit. R7 is a little less straight forward, and the same technique, but with this component above R6 with its upper end connected to pin 2 of IC1 via a track taken between pins 1 and 8 of IC1 will not work since this track would cross over the positive supply track. Of course, printed circuit tracks cannot cross one another without a connection between the two (except by using a double sided board that is).

The simple solution is to position R6 so that it crosses over the positive supply track to IC1. There is then no difficulty with a track connecting the right hand side of R7 to pin 6 of IC1 and the left hand leadout wire being connected to pin 2 of IC1 via a second track. Such a simple solution is not always possible, and it might be necessary to rearrange the positions of several components in order to fit everything in properly, or there may be no alternative to using a link wire on the component side of the board. Although most printed circuit designers try to avoid using link wires this is sometimes unavoidable, and in other cases one or two link wires can enable a much simpler track pattern to be used. When using simple methods of printed circuit production it is probably more practical to opt for link wires and a less complex track pattern. A technique which if often useful is to take tracks between the pads of an integrated circuit, but a drawback to this method is the narrow (0.1 inch) spacing of DIL integrated circuit pins. This leaves very little space for the track to pass between the pads without short circuiting to one of them, and makes boards of this type difficult to produce using simple constructional methods. However, with care it is possible to produce such boards using even the most simple of constructional methods.

Returning to the printed circuit layout once again, the next component to draw in place is D1 which should logically go to the right of IC1, vertically, and with its cathode (+) leadout wire towards the positive supply rail and its anode terminal near to pin 6 of IC1. Tr1 is the last component, and is situated to the right of D1 close to the positive supply rail, with its collector terminal on the positive supply line. The tracks to connect D1 to IC1 and Tr1 are then added to the drawing.

Finally the connections to off-board components PB1 and B1 must be drawn in. Wiring the board to such components is easier if the connections are made to the edge of the board rather than somewhere in the middle. Taking these connections out to the edge of the board, or close to the edge of the board does not usually cause any difficulties. It is also helpful if the connection points for each off-board component are grouped together, and with components such as potentiometers the connection to the central tag of the component should ideally be the one in the centre of the group of connection points on the board. Again, this is not usually too difficult to achieve in practice, and it does not matter too much if it cannot be achieved. However, make sure that the drawing makes the correct method of connection to off-board components quite clear if there is any possibility of a mistake being made here.

Figure 11 shows the completed printed circuit design for the electronic doorbuzzer circuit. Corner markers showing the edges of the board are included in the diagram, and the board has been made large enough to take a couple of mounting holes. I prefer not to have mounting holes in amongst the components unless this is necessary in order to keep down the size of the board, but provided there is a reasonable amount of the space for the mounting holes and they can be positioned where they will provide a firm mounting for the board it is quite acceptable

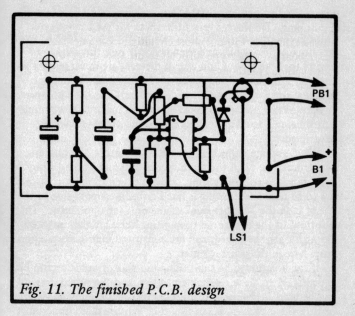

*Fig. 11. The finished P.C.B. design*

to put them at any convenient place on the board. For small boards of up to about 100mm by 50mm two mounting holes are usually sufficient to provide a strong mounting, but with larger boards it is preferable to use three or four mounting holes.

If the board is to fit into guide rails in a case rather than being bolted in place it will be necessary to design the board to be a certain size so that it fits into the case properly. This is not really very difficult provided you bear in mind the limitations on the size of the board when doing the design work, and provided the board can be large enough to comfortably accommodate all the components. Remember that a few millimetres at each end of the board must be free of components in order to enable the board to slot into place properly, and if the case is a metal type the ends of the board must be free of copper tracks as well (so that these are not short circuited through the case).

## Making the Board

Once you have completed the drawing it is a good idea to put it
to one side for a while and then check it very thoroughly to
ensure that the layout and circuit diagram are in agreement and
that no errors have been made. It is much easier to correct
errors at this stage than it is once the board has been completed.
A simple error at the drawing stage could result in the completed
board being wasted and a new one having to be etched and
assembled.

When you are sure that everything is correct, the board is
constructed in much the same way as building a board from a
design in a book or magazine. If a resist pen or resist transfers
are to be used the drawing is fixed onto the copper side of the
board with the "copper side" of the drawing uppermost. The
positions of the component mounting holes are then marked
through onto the board, and the construction process progresses
from here in the usual manner.

If the board is to be built using the photographic method it
is necessary to draw a suitable positive, and the pencil drawing
can be used as the basis of this positive. It is merely necessary
to turn the drawing over so that it is "copper side" uppermost,
and then rub-on transfers or die-cut symbols are used to add
the pads to the drawing, after which the tracks are laid down
using rub-on transfers or drafting tapes. The use of these
materials was covered in the previous chapter and this will not be
covered again here. When producing the positive it will probably
be easier to make a neat job of it if the pencil drawing is
repositioned accurately on the precision grid after the drawing
has been turned "copper side" uppermost.

Once the positive has been completed it is advisable to
remove the pencil marks on the "component side" of the
drawing. These would probably be too faint to cause any
problems when making the exposure, but it is better not to risk
spoiling a board and to remove them. They can be carefully
removed using an ordinary eraser, or a piece of wet kitchen paper
plus some soap or detergent can be employed. Spirit based
cleaners are not recommended since they might dissolve and
damage the drafting film. Of course, if a sketch of the componer

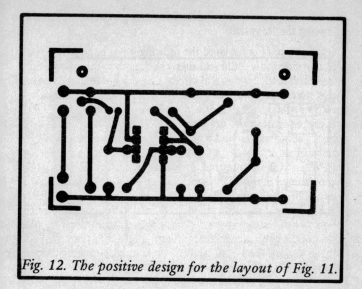

*Fig. 12. The positive design for the layout of Fig. 11.*

layout is needed to assist with the final assembly of the board this should be made prior to cleaning off the pencil markings. For the printed circuit design of Figure 11 this gives a positive design as shown in Figure 12, and a component layout sketch as shown in Figure 13. The board is then produced in the normal way.

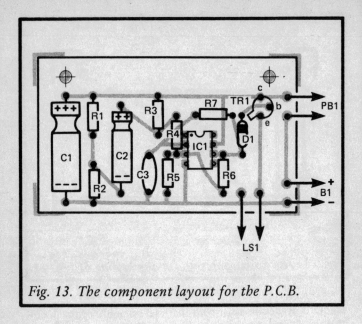

*Fig. 13. The component layout for the P.C.B.*

66

*Notes*

*Notes*